WOLFGANG AMADEUS MOZART

LE NOZZE DI FIGARO
THE MARRIAGE OF FIGARO
DIE HOCHZEIT DES FIGARO

Overture to the Opera
K 492

Edited by/Herausgegeben von
Hermann Abert

T0081242

Ernst Eulenburg Ltd

London · Mainz · Madrid · New York · Paris · Prague · Tokyo · Toronto · Zürich

LE NOZZE DI FIGARO

Overture

Wolfgang Amadeus Mozart
(1756–1791)
K 492

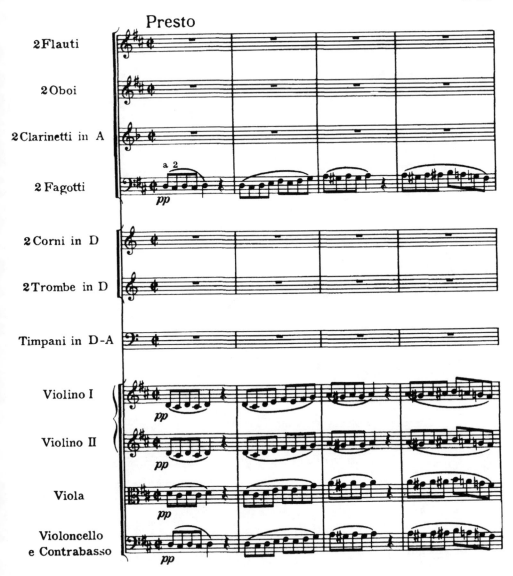

No. 603   EE 3703

2

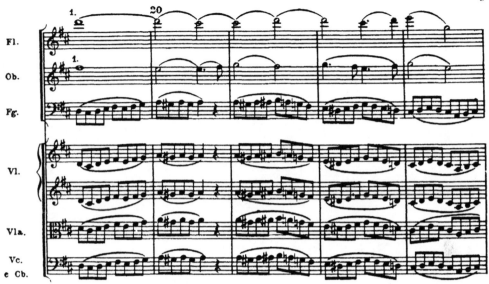

4

9

170

18

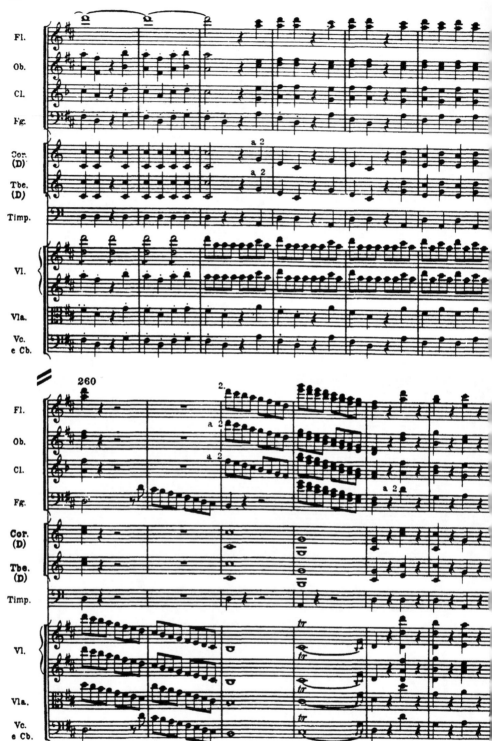

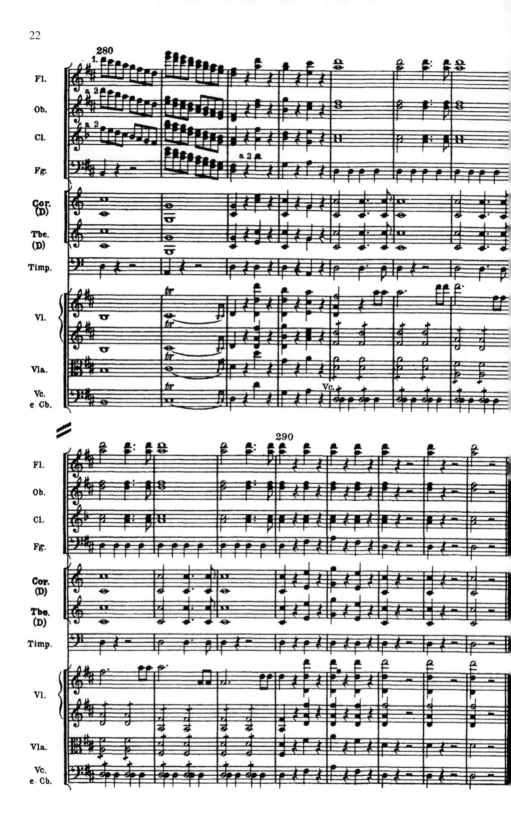